CinDer Finn's Fairy Godmother

Written by
Gail Baccelli Major

Illustrated by Teresa Wilkerson

CinDer Finn's Fairy Godmother
Written by Gail Baccelli Major
Illustrated by Teresa Wilkerson
Book Design by Tara Sizemore
Published November 2020
Skippy Creek
Imprint of Jan-Carol Publishing, Inc

Copyright © Gail Baccelli Major
ISBN: 978-1-950895-73-1
Library of Congress Control Number: 2020950468

You may contact the publisher:
Jan-Carol Publishing, Inc.
PO Box 701
Johnson City, TN 37605
publisher@jancarolpublishing.com
www.jancarolpublishing.com

Jan-Carol
Publishing, Inc
"every story needs a book"

This book is dedicated to my Auntie.
She has always been my "Queen of Hearts."

No matter what each of us is going through in our lives, we always come together in thought, words, or deeds. We have a profound bond. However, each of us has so much love for so many people. Maybe that's why we can get such a heavy heart when sorrow comes our way. My Auntie always has a way of lifting me up.

With her quiet spirit and grace, she has always made my heart smile. She is so lovely. Life has changed through the years. She is retired now and lives in Florida with her beloved husband, William, and her fur child, Lola.

I transformed the ring into a pendant and gave it to my Auntie's daughter, Sarah. It was time for her to enjoy it in a different way. I know she will cherish it in memory of her dad and my godfather, Richard.

I hope the ring holds for her all the love it held for me. It is an heirloom piece for certain.

God bless Auntie and William and their beautiful families.

Hugs and kisses,
Gail Marie

With Love,
Gail

Let me introduce myself. My name is CinDer Finn.

That's right, Finn—F-i-n-n. l live in a world of pretend.

l am a Princess Dolphin.

On the nights of a full moon, I must make my way to the water. Something very mystical and magical happens to me when I look to the light of the moon.

I transform into this most delightful, playful dolphin!

How I love to dive deep into the clear, blue green water.

I often come up and do spirals in the air. What fun! Other dolphins come from near and far. They can hear my call. They want to join in on all the action. My existence is never boring. God sends me out on all kinds of assignments. The hearts in need find me, or I find them. I never know exactly where I am going or where I will end up. I trust he knows.

Of course, I stay in close contact with the Archangels Michael, Gabriel, Uriel, and Raphael. They assist me along the way by dropping pennies along my path. Believe you me, I do need them to stay the path of a light worker. When I go out into the world, I walk as a humble servant ready to assist the needs of others.

It is only through the eyes of the children that I become a princess. You could say, I am on a kind of mission. Or so it seems. Well, I have been waiting to tell you something very exciting. You are not going to believe this one. I have a real live fairy godmother. Did you hear me? I know, sounds a little far fetched. What do you think of that?

My fairy godmother lived over in England, her homeland. Can you imagine traveling from all that distance and finding me. Well, she did. Tell me—isn't that magical? She is the Queen of Hearts, especially in my eyes. For she does not carry a magical wand with her. She carries a magical touch with whomever she's with and wherever she goes. I have felt it many times. It is very real. That is her great gift given by God. Her touch goes directly to the heart.

My fairy godmother has always been my greatest inspiration. She is lots of fun! You are not going to believe the gift she gave me one day. That's right, a gift given with love, a gift never expected. Her mere presence has always been more than enough for me. I always love being around her. She gave me this brilliant, sparkling cluster of magnificent diamonds. It takes on the shape of a wonderful teardrop. I call it my princess ring.

When I go on assignments, the children stare at it.

They sense it is mystical and has magic powers.

Well, they are right. Within each of the fifty-five stones,

lies a spectacular ray of light. At times it is blinding.

It reminds me of this great beacon—my very own

compass. Perhaps it helps direct me to the souls I need

to reach. The power that it holds is the greatest power of

all. That being...the "Power of Love." All I have to do is look

into the ring and my heart is warmed. I tell the children to

believe, it is from my fairy godmother. Do you know what

they say? They all wish they had a fairy godmother. I tell

them I am blessed to have her.

My fairy godmother chose me, she didn't have to. She has always been there for me. She has seen me on my knees and she has seen me standing. She has witnessed my greatest joys and my greatest pain. I know at times it must have been hard for her to watch, when I needed to go my own path. I'm sure it was frightening to her. No matter what circumstance I managed to get myself into, just the tone of her voice was soothing enough to know everything would be alright.

I remember when my fairy godmother first appeared to me, an earth angel, all in white, on her wedding day. What a glorious vision. She stood so statuesque. She looked like a goddess. She was radiant. She wore this beautiful, white, flowing gown and her hair was all pinned up in an entwining twist. Her big blue eyes were pierced through me. Her smile lit up the whole room. I stood there frozen. I could not move. In that moment, she did not seem human.

My fairy godmother has moved away to warmer climate, where she belongs. She is too warm hearted for cold weather. God sends her on her own assignments assisting the elderly, for in service, she is a nurse. I will always adore her, even when she is very, very old. I always ask the angels to keep a special eye on her. They understand.

So maybe if you believe, you too will one day have a fairy godmother, if you don't have one already. Just think for a moment. Has there ever been anyone in your life who has been like a fairy godmother?

Maybe your fairy godmother has been there all along.

You will know, you will feel the love and magic!

Acknowledgments

For the love of God, for the love of friends and family, I am grateful. For my husband, our children, and grandson, I am blessed. I pray for this world to come back together in union and of the United States of America.

Through the Eyes of a Mother and the Heart of a Child, it is my greatest hope—for our highest best and good, in love and light for all humanity, in decency of our common thread and the need of each other. So lean in, Dear God, lean in.

About the Author

Gail Baccelli Major lives in Warren, Rhode Island with her devoted husband, Bob. It was Gail's love for children's books and reading that brought her heart to a place to take classes and to develop a book. To fill her time, she focuses on heartfelt and soulful projects. One of the best things Gail ever did was open a book, and she strives to encourage a love of reading in all. Readers can contact her by email: gailbaccellimajor05@gmail.com.

At left, in recognition of the beautiful yellow Swiss polka dot dress made with love from my beloved Mother, with matching hat.

CPSIA information can be obtained
at www.ICGtesting.com
Printed in the USA
JSHW052315180121
11041JS00002B/4